MW00576553

Praise for *Please Explain Alzheimer's Disease to Me: A Children's Story and Parent Handbook About Dementia*

"With *Please Explain Alzheimer's Disease to Me: A Children's Story and Parent Handbook About Dementia*, Dr. Zelinger provides a valuable, evidence-based resource for introducing children to this complex and challenging topic. This engaging book provides important information in a user-friendly format and offers adults the foundation for easily engaging children in what may initially seem like a very difficult discussion. The *Tips for Families* and *Q & As* are particularly useful features for adults, to which they can return periodically as needs change and new questions arise. By combining a children's book and a handbook for parents, Dr. Zelinger has created a single resource about Alzheimer's disease that I will be sure to recommend to everyone I know in the 'sandwich generation.'"

Shane S. Bush, Ph.D., ABPP, board certified in geropsychology, clinical neuropsychology, clinical psychology and rehabilitation psychology; president, American Board of Geropsychology

"Dr. Zelinger has written a book that helps take the mystery out of a truly mystifying disease. In a thoughtful and comprehensive way, Dr. Zelinger explains Alzheimer's to both children and adults facing a loved one with this disorder. The children's story will help reduce the anxiety and fear a they may have when faced with one suffering from Alzheimer's, and the adult portion of this book provides practical examples to help guide them when questions arise. A truly informative and inspired book."

Marilyn Cherney, occupational therapist; grandmother

"Filled with just the right number of facts and feelings, this handbook is an impactful, practical guide for anyone. Dr. Zelinger recognizes the universality of this disease, yet personalizes it with anecdotes, tips and Q & As so that you are empowered and better able to deal emotionally. This handbook hits your head and heart and is a must "go-to" book for Alzheimer's. As a mother with 8 children, I found this book to be the singular resource needed by families with young children who are in the position of having to explain this disease."

Kim DiLuzio

"Dr. Zelinger's thoughtful and practical book provides a story that children can relate to and a guide for parents to better explain what is happening to those who suffer from dementia. The book creates an atmosphere for emotionally intelligent conversation about the changes that happen to the person they love. *Please Explain Alzheimer's Disease to Me* is an excellent resource to assist families with this difficult to explain, but loving family dynamic."

Bruce Alster, Star Factor emotional intelligence leadership coach and retired principal

"A much needed book to explain a difficult topic to our children and ourselves. Dr. Zelinger's warmth, insight and clinical judgment shine through her every page! This is a superlative book that will get front row billing on my office bookshelf."

Deborah Lief-Dienstag MD, FAAP, pediatrician

"Finally! A book to explain Alzheimer's disease to children in an easy-to-understand, developmentally appropriate manner! As a nurse and mental health counselor, I know how much this book is needed, as Alzheimer's disease impacts almost 6 million adults. *Please Explain Alzheimer's Disease to Me* not only offers children a chance to understand the many changes that a loved one may experience due to Alzheimer's disease, but also offers resources for adults to have meaningful conversations with their child. Zelinger's book even includes a kid-friendly explanation of the changes that happen in the brain because of Alzheimer's disease! There are many changes children need to understand and adapt to when a loved one has Alzheimer's disease, and *Please Explain Alzheimer's Disease to Me* is a gentle and realistic way to begin those difficult conversations. Parents will find the tips for families, and the question and answer section, especially helpful."

Casey O'Brien Martin, LMHC, REAT, RN, author of *Skills for Big Feelings: A Guide for Teaching Kids Relaxation, Regulation, and Coping Techniques*

"From growing up with grandparents with Alzheimer's disease, to now caring for thousands of residents with Alzheimer's disease, I truly wish this book was given to me 30 years ago. Dr. Zelinger takes a painful topic for both children and parents alike and turns it into a beautiful story and a detailed handbook that gives us the tools we need to broach a topic we all hope to never have to face. This book is a must read for families facing the challenges that come along with a loved one experiencing Alzheimer's disease."

Avi Satt, president, Allegria Senior Living

"*Please Explain Alzheimer's Disease to Me* is a wonderful resource for families looking to help children understand their loved one's Alzheimer's/dementia condition. It is a touching portrayal of the changing relationship between children and a grandmother living with dementia. The book also includes valuable answers to common questions and further reading suggestions following the story."

Grace Bazile M.S.L.I.S. Peninsula Public Library

Please Explain "Alzheimer's Disease" to Me

A CHILDREN'S STORY AND PARENT HANDBOOK ABOUT DEMENTIA

LAURIE ZELINGER, PH.D

Loving Healing Press
Ann Arbor, MI

Please Explain Alzheimer's Disease to Me: A Children's Story and Parent Handbook About Dementia
Copyright © 2021 by Laurie Zelinger, PhD, ABPP, MS, RPT-S

Illustrations by Bijan Sammadar

Library of Congress Cataloging-in-Publication Data

Names: Zelinger, Laurie, 1952- author.
Title: Please explain Alzheimer's disease to me : a children's story and
   parent handbook about dementia / Laurie Zelinger, PhD, ABPP, MS., RPT-S.

Description: Ann Arbor, MI : Loving Healing Press, [2021] | Includes
   bibliographical references. | Audience: Ages 5-8 years | Audience:
   Grades 2-3 | Summary: "This book, a complete and practical resource for
   children and adults facing Alzheimer's in their family, introduces the
   subject matter to children in a colorful, sensitive and gentle story,
   followed by a parent/caregiver section which supplies comprehensive
   information which adults can use to understand and plan for the course
   of the disease affecting their loved one"-- Provided by publisher.
Identifiers: LCCN 2021026302 (print) | LCCN 2021026303 (ebook) | ISBN
   9781615995912 (paperback) | ISBN 9781615995929 (hardcover) | ISBN
   9781615995936 (epub) | ISBN 9781615995936 (epub)
Subjects: LCSH: Alzheimer's disease--Juvenile literature. |
   Dementia--Juvenile literature.
Classification: LCC RC523 .Z454 2021 (print) | LCC RC523 (ebook) | DDC
   616.8/311--dc23
LC record available at https://lccn.loc.gov/2021026302
LC ebook record available at https://lccn.loc.gov/2021026303

ISBN 978-1-61599-591-2 paperback
ISBN 978-1-61599-592-9 hardcover
ISBN 978-1-61599-593-6 eBook

Published by
Loving Healing Press
5145 Pontiac Trail
Ann Arbor, MI 48105

www.LHPress.com
info@LHPress.com

Tollfree 888-761-6268
FAX 734-663-6861

Distributed by
Ingram (USA/CAN/AU), Betram's Books (UK/EU)

DEDICATION

This book is dedicated to:

My grandmother, Anna, who invented words when she could not summon the ones she wanted, and who so aptly created "cloggy" to describe a dreary day filled with clouds and fog.

My mother, Shirley, a scientist, who described her vanishing memory as her greatest loss. Both of these women lived and died with dementia.

My father, Simon, who liked to say that at age 103, "I still have most of my marbles" (and he did!) but who asked me to share with my readers that, "Old people want to be remembered as they were, not as they are now." He passed away when this book was in its final stage of production.

…and to the baby boom generation.

Other Great Parenting Books in the *Please Explain* Series by Laurie Zelinger, PhD

Please Explain Anxiety to Me: Simple Biology and Solutions for Children and Parents

Please Explain Tonsillectomy & Adenoidectomy to Me: A Complete Guide to Preparing Your Child for Surgery

Please Explain Terrorism to Me! A Story for Children, P-E-A-R-L-S of Wisdom for Their Parents

Please Explain Time Out to Me! A Story for Children and Do-it-Yourself Manual for Parents

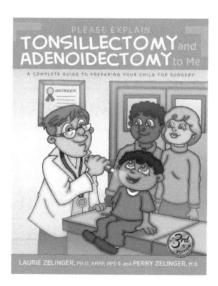

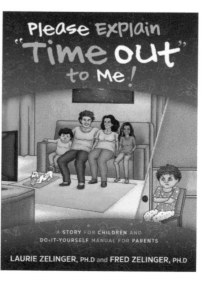

CONTENT

Introduction

In 2020, almost 6 million adults in the United States were living with Alzheimer's disease, the most common form of dementia, and that number is rising sharply. Because you selected this book, it is likely that you know, or are caring for, somebody with this degenerative disease. It is also likely that you have a young child in your life who may have questions about this illness; in fact, it is estimated that 25% of people caring for an individual with Alzheimer's disease are also caring for children, earning those caregivers membership in the sandwich generation.

This book was written to provide both children and adults with information about dementia that would be helpful to them based on their unique perspectives. The children's story provides a gentle and engaging context in which to understand expected changes in a grandparent, while the Parent/Caregiver Handbook at the back of the book offers facts, figures, practical suggestions, answers to common questions and resources for having meaningful conversations with a young child. It is my hope that this book will help families understand and navigate the aging process when dementia takes hold of a loved one.

A Story for Children

My name is Seth and this is my cousin, Shepard, but we call him Shep for short. I get to see my cousin on weekends, when we go to our grandmother's house for Sunday dinner. We have so much fun playing together, and just about always, one of the grownups tells us we're making too much noise or says, "No running in the house!" It's always the same.

Every Sunday, Grandma makes chicken soup, meat, potatoes and noodles. And she buys our favorite cake for dessert. It's always the same, and I like it that way.

Last time we were there, Shep was hiding in the kitchen, and I went to look for him when something hysterical happened. All of a sudden, Grandma's refrigerator started to ring! And it kept ringing. We opened the door and guess what? We saw Grandma's phone in there, right next to the cream cheese! We laughed so hard that I got a pain in my side.

Mom came in to make sure we weren't getting into trouble and I told her about the phone. She didn't think it was so funny. In fact, she didn't laugh one tiny bit. She made a weird face and walked into the other room. Shep and I kept playing, and since it was my turn to hide, I squeezed behind the couch. When I peeked out, I saw my mother whispering to my aunt. They both looked worried.

Somebody said dinner was ready, and we all sat down in our regular places. Grandma sat near the kitchen, and Shep sat next to me. It's always the same, and I like it that way. The food was delicious. Except for the potatoes. They were burnt. Grandma said she forgot to turn off the oven and they cooked so long that the house got smoky. That part wasn't the same.

I love dessert but I still get excited for dinner to be over anyway. That's when Grandma gives us a little prize that she bought at the 99 cent store she always goes to, and we get to play with it while the grownups talk and clean up. Shep and I waited and waited and waited, but Grandma never gave us a prize that night.

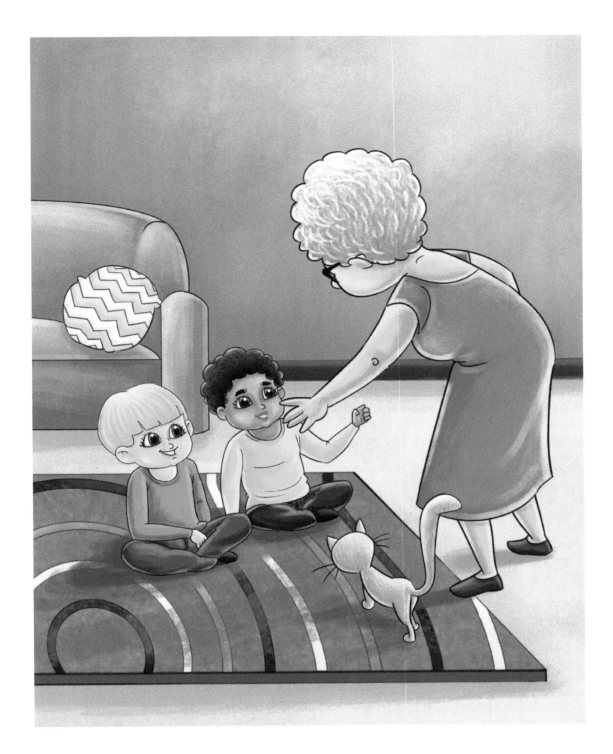

I'm not spoiled, and I know I shouldn't always expect a present, but it's always the same, and I like it that way. In my most polite voice, I asked Grandma if she went to the 99 cent store this week. She gave me a hug and said that she tried to, but then she got lost on the way and ended up walking around the neighborhood for a long time. By the time she figured out how to get home, she forgot what she went out for. Grandma never got lost before. That part wasn't the same.

We didn't go to Grandma's house the next Sunday or the one after that. But when we did go back, my mother and my aunt cooked dinner instead, while Grandma sat quietly by a window.

At mealtime there was another change. Mom sat next to the kitchen and Grandma sat in a different seat. Things looked a little mixed up. Grandma said Mom's cooking was good, but not as good as hers, and we all laughed. She tried to tell us how she learned to cook when she was a little girl, but her story got confusing, because she kept saying the wrong words and forgot some people's names. I was starting to feel weird watching Grandma act this way.

Back at home that night, Mom told me that she saw me watching Grandma. She asked how I   was feeling and if there was anything I wanted to talk about. I didn't want to be rude or say anything bad, but I knew something was different, and I was a little scared to say it out loud. Mom knew what I was thinking and tried to explain it to me.

She told me that Grandma has a special kind of forgetting. It's different from the kind of forgetting that we all have sometimes. Everybody forgets some stuff, like when I forgot to do my math homework, or brush my teeth or where I put my favorite video game. That's normal because it happens to everyone. But Grandma's kind of forgetting is different.

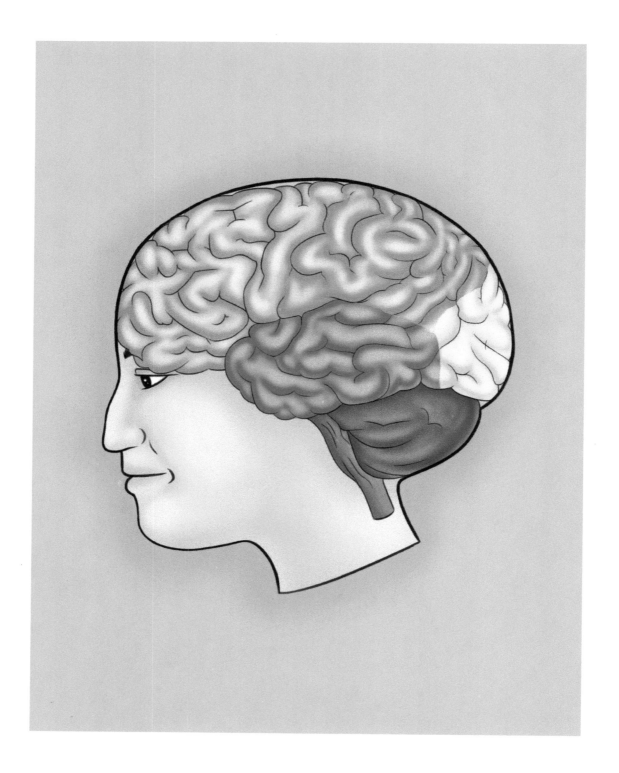

Grandma's brain is changing because she has something called Alzheimer's disease (Its pronounced '*alts hy merz*'). Some people call it dementia (and that's pronounced '*duh men shuh*'). It just happens, by itself, to some people when they get old. But it doesn't happen to everybody. We can't catch it or anything. Mom drew a picture of a brain for me and it looked like this. Then, she described how Grandma's brain was different.

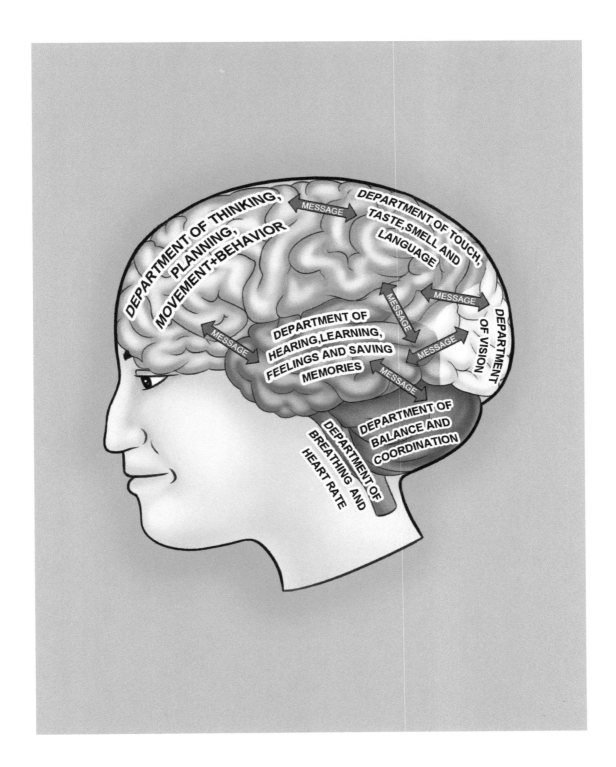

She explained that our brains are in charge of everything in our body and the different parts have different jobs. It's kind of like the different places at school that are for different activities. All the departments are separate, but sometimes they have to send each other messages and work together.

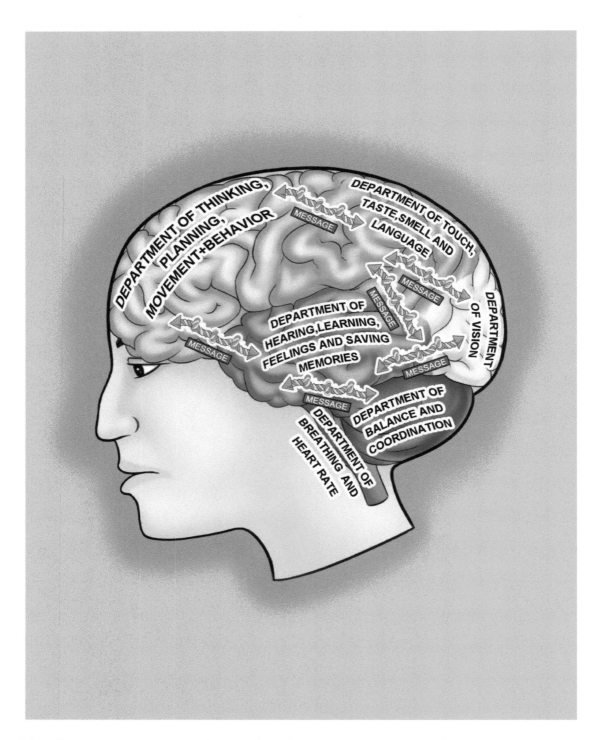

Mom said when one part of our brain wants to send a message to another department the message goes through special pathways. But the departments in Grandma's brain aren't working the way they used to. It is harder for them to get messages and so she gets confused. Her pathways are getting clogged and tangled up, kind of like the way my hair gets after we wash it. Mom said we can get the knots out of my hair by brushing it, but there is no way to get the tangles out of Grandma's brain. Wouldn't it be so cool if we could wave a magic wand and say, "Abracadabra ABC, get rid of Grandma's tangles 1-2-3!"

I found out that Grandma will forget more and more things but will probably remember things from the olden days better. She will need help doing the things that she used to do for everyone else, and she might get grouchy more often. Medicine will help a little, but nobody can make Alzheimer's go away. It can't be fixed or get better or go back to the way it was before.

One day, Grandma might need other grown-ups to go to her house to help her. She might even come to live with us or with Shep or my other aunt and uncle. Or maybe there will be a different, special place that will be just right for her instead. That part won't be the same, and I probably won't like it...but I will get used to it.

I felt sad and scared and thought about ways I could help. Mom told me that if Grandma's mind and body stay active, it might help a little. Then, I remembered how we used to play some word games together, like thinking of a food that starts with each letter of the alphabet. The last time we played, Grandma picked artichoke, I picked banana and then she said cake, because she knows that's my favorite dessert. We got all the way to the letter Q but then had to stop because we couldn't think of anything.

I decided I can read to Grandma and teach her how to use new apps on her cell phone. I can make a photo album with pictures of Shep and me and all my aunts and uncles, and I can make her a memory wallet with important information about herself and our family. And I can help her write addresses on the envelopes she has to mail.

I will tell Grandma stories, teach her words I learn in other languages and sing songs that I know she likes. We can do exercises together, and when she has trouble walking, I can push her wheelchair. Maybe we will even go to the 99 cent store together. I will remind Grandma how much I love her, even if she doesn't remember me.

We will still see Grandma on Sundays. Shep and I will still get yelled at for running around and making too much noise and somebody will make dinner. We have to make sure that we all eat healthy food, so from now on, vegetables and fish will be on the table, too, right next to the meat and potatoes. Some things will be different but a lot of things will still be the same. I like it that way.

Parent/Caregiver Handbook

This section is devoted to you. Perhaps you have already read quite a bit about dementia on your own, or perhaps your knowledge about this disease is limited. I am hoping to provide you with enough information to begin a conversation, answer your child's questions and perhaps even address some of your own. It will be up to you to decide what to share regarding your personal situation. Usually, it is best to share just the most basic facts with your child, adding details as their interest and curiosity dictate. But as an adult, you may want to learn more about the course of this illness in order to feel best prepared. The following pages, which are quite scientific, are provided as a resource for you. After you read and digest the passages, you can take the information that pertains to your circumstances and customize it to your child's developmental level.

Talking to your Kids

It is often best to start with a statement rather than a question that describes what the child has already observed. For example, "I think we all noticed that Grandma seemed very confused today. She kept calling me by the wrong name," or "Grandpa was very irritable today. That must have been upsetting to see." Then, wait and see what your child says. If your child remains quiet, you might ask, "What are you wondering about? How do you feel when you see Grandma/Grandpa acting this way?" Find out what your child already knows, what they are thinking about and what misconceptions they may have. It is important to let them know that they can say whatever they want, even if it is scary or unkind. You don't want them censoring their thoughts if you want to have an honest dialogue. Allow plenty of time for this important conversation, and let your child know they can bring it up again whenever they choose. You don't have to know all the answers. But you do want to set the stage for your kids to feel comfortable enough to hear what you have to say, to ask the questions they ponder and to be able to maintain a loving relationship with the important person in their life who has become ill.

Facts and Figures

Dementia is a brain disease and is the overall term used to describe a specific group of degenerative symptoms that include memory loss, problems with language, thinking, reasoning, attention, planning and judgment. It is often accompanied by personality changes and a decline in overall functioning that impairs a person's ability to function in daily life (Alzheimer's Association Report, 2020; Arvanitakis & Bennett, 2019; Mayo Clinic, n.d.).

Alzheimer's disease, discovered in 1906, is just one form of dementia but there are others, and when two or more occur at the same time it is referred to as mixed dementia. Alzheimer's disease, the most familiar and common form of dementia, accounts for 60-80 percent of cases and is listed as the fifth leading cause of death among Americans over age 65 (Alzheimer's Association Report, 2019). Late onset Alzheimer's refers to the diagnosis when it is applied to individuals over age 65, whereas early onset refers to persons younger than 65. "Though the greatest known risk factor for Alzheimer's is increasing age, the disease is not a normal part of aging. And though most people with Alzheimer's are 65 and older, approximately 200,000 Americans under 65 have younger-onset Alzheimer's disease" [Alzheimer's Association n.d., Dementia vs. Alzheimer's disease). While genetics and family history of the disease are contributory, its cause is not known. "About 25 % of Americans have a copy of the Alzheimer's gene-APOEe4-tripling their risk of getting the disease" (Harrar, S. 2017).

It is believed that the brain begins changing anywhere from 10 to 20 years before symptoms appear, and an accurate diagnosis is difficult to determine in a living individual, as a definitive diagnosis can only be made upon autopsy. However, advances in science and medicine suggest that neuropsychological tests, lab work, spinal taps and brain scan imaging are becoming reliable predictors in the identification of individuals who are at risk for developing the disease. These should begin early, especially in people with a strong family history or with a first degree relative who has had dementia. However, not all memory loss and confusion are attributed to Alzheimer's disease. Often referred to as a "senior moment," a certain amount of forgetfulness is expected with aging, and is not necessarily a symptom of this diagnosis. In addition, other diseases, head trauma, infections, immune disorders, stroke, metabolic problems, endocrine abnormalities, medication side effects, nutritional deficiencies and other issues may be responsible for similar symptoms, some of which are reversible (Mayo clinic).

The Progression of Alzheimer's Disease

Worldwide, the average lifespan of a person is estimated to be 71.1 years. The United States exceeds that number, with an average lifespan of nearly 79 years (Kluger & Sifferlin, 2018). As the baby boom generation matures and reaches advanced age, the population of older Americans is growing, as is the number of cases of dementia.

The degenerative feature of Alzheimer's disease is its progression from pre-clinical symptoms to noticeable, mild cognitive impairment, before embarking upon the moderate and severe stages of the disease over a course of years or decades. Alzheimer's disease is characterized by brain changes that involve two types of abnormal changes to brain cells. One change is a buildup of beta-amyloid protein clusters (referred to as plaque), which gather in the spaces between the nerve cells. The other is the buildup of protein tau tangles within the cell walls (Weir, 2017). When the tau proteins break down, they leave the equivalent of "potholes" in the neural pathways that are needed for conduction of messages. "With this communication flow disrupted, nerve cells start to wither and die..." (Park, 2010). Medication has been shown to be helpful in slowing down the rate of deterioration, but Alzheimer's disease cannot be reversed or cured. It is widely agreed that certain lifestyle practices may slow the decline. Those positive influences include: a heart healthy diet, good sleep hygiene, physical movement, elimination of smoking, control of hypertension and diabetes, maintaining social relationships, engaging in leisure activities, stimulating one's brain with books, puzzles and complex work (brain fitness), engaging in conversation and advancing one's education (Alzheimer's Association Reports 2019 and 2020; Arvanitakis & Bennett; Munson, M., 2017; Smith, G., 2016; and Mayo Clinic).

Medication

At this time, only five drugs have been approved by the U.S. Food and Drug Administration for the treatment of Alzheimer's disease: rivastigmine, galantamine, donepezil, memantine and a combination of the last two (Alzheimer's Association, 2020). Several trials of anticipated new drugs have not delivered promising results in recent years for people with early symptoms, but science is still trying to understand the cause of dementia and find ways to attack the plaque and tangles effectively. Sometimes, other medications are prescribed to address secondary symptoms that may accompany dementia. Those problematic issues include depression, hallucinations, anxiety, restlessness and sleep disorders (Ingram, 2003).

Stages and Symptoms

Alzheimer's disease is often described as having three stages: mild, moderate and severe. However, Dr. Barry Reisberg at New York University/ Langone Hospital developed the Global Deterioration Scale, also referred to as the Reisberg Scale, which delineates seven stages (Herndon, 2019). In the first stage (1) there is no report of any cognitive decline followed by the **very mild cognitive decline** stage (2) where names and words may be forgotten and objects misplaced. In the **mild decline phase** (3) there may be some trouble completing tasks at work or comprehending what is read. The **moderate** decline stage (4) describes increased forgetting about one's personal history and inability to complete complex tasks, as well as changes in mood and personality.

In the **moderately severe** stage (5), there are significant memory voids and help is needed in managing daily activities. At this stage, there is confusion about dates, times and places, difficulty recalling one's address and phone number and problems with decision making. The phase marking **severe cognitive decline** (6) includes losing awareness of surroundings and recent experiences, forgetting names of caregivers, changes in sleep patterns and difficulty managing toileting procedures independently. In its final **very severe cognitive decline** phase (7), eating, swallowing, toileting, ambulation and conversational skills are non-functional. The individual becomes fully dependent in all aspects of their care and may require support to sit or combat the rigidity that affects movement of their muscles.

Trajectory

Individuals over age 65 with Alzheimer's live, on average, four to eight years after being diagnosed; however, many survive longer. By age 80, it is estimated that 75% of those with the disease live in a nursing home, compared with 4% of people in the same age group without the disease (Alzheimer's Association, 2020). A Yale University study "found that in a group of 4,765 people with an average age of 72, those who carried a gene variant linked to dementia- but who also had positive attitudes about aging- were 50% less likely to develop the disorder than people who carried the gene but faced aging with more pessimism or fear" (Kluger & Sifferlin).

It was recently reported that about 50 million people worldwide have some form of dementia (Park, 2016; Kivipelto & Hakansson, 2017). Now, as the baby boom generation ages, the incidence of Alzheimer's disease is increasing sharply. In 2020, 5.8 million Americans over the age of 65 (one in 10) had this disease (Park, 2018). It affected 3 % of people in the 65-74 age bracket, 17% of people age 75-84 and 32% of people over the age of 85 (Alzheimer's Association 2020). The Alzheimer's Association estimates that by 2025, that number will reach 7.1 million and by 2050, it will soar to 13.8 million.

It is reported that certain individuals are more susceptible to Alzheimer's disease. "Older black/African Americans and Hispanics/Latinos are disproportionately more likely than older whites to have Alzheimer's or other dementias" (Alzheimer's Association, 2020; Smith). In addition, individuals with Down syndrome appear vulnerable at an earlier age than others without Down syndrome (Ingram). Women make up two-thirds of the Alzheimer's population (3.6 million), whereas men comprise 2.2 million.

Medical Support

A recent study found that 85% of people first diagnosed with dementia were usually given the diagnosis by a primary care physician rather than a dementia specialist. "In 2016, there were 7,293 certified geriatricians in the United States, or one geriatrician for every 1,924 Americans age of 65 or older in need of care" (Alzheimer's Association, 2020). Additionally, in 2017, Medicare began to reimburse medical practitioners for health care visits that culminated in a comprehensive dementia plan. People with Alzheimer's often require more skilled nursing care and home health visits, while also experiencing twice the number of hospitalizations as others in the same age group without the disease. "The lifetime cost of care for individuals with Alzheimer's dementia was more than twice the amount incurred by individuals without Alzheimer's dementia...Total payments in 2020 for all individuals with Alzheimer's or other dementias are estimated at 305 billion, not including the value of informal caregiving..." (Alzheimer's Association, 2020). It is reported that 83% of the care provided to those affected is supplied by family, friends and unpaid workers, two-thirds of whom are women. According to the National Academy of Sciences, Engineering and Medicine, 17.7 million people, or approximately 7.7 percent of the total U.S. population aged 20 and older, were caregivers of an older adult in 2011.

Caregivers

Caregivers report that caring for someone with Alzheimer's is more time intensive than caring for someone without the disease (approximately 92 hours per month vs. 65). Increased stress levels in the caretaker often coincide with the patient's increased need for supervision. Reportedly, 6 out of 10 people with Alzheimer's will wander at least once, become disoriented and become lost, making their supervision a critical task (Alzheimer's Association 2019, Wandering and getting lost). Caregivers often report their own depression, interruptions in their ability to work, health problems, higher rates of chronic disease, more use of over the counter and prescription medications and financial impact. Dr. Riffin, psychologist at Weill Cornell, refers to caregivers as the "invisible patients" who are "often overburdened by their caregiving responsibilities" (Amazing Advances in Research, Technology, and Patient care, 2018). More than half of caretakers with children under the age of 18 who were surveyed indicated that caring for someone with Alzheimer's was more difficult than caring for a child. For some, the obligations are compounded. Twenty-five percent of caretakers find themselves in the sandwich generation, caring for significant others of both younger and older generations.

Alzheimer's takes its toll on the patient as well as on the family, with increased support and supervision vying for a caretaker's time, attention and money against the backdrop of emotional upheaval. It is an illness that does not get better and lasts for years, sometimes even decades. Its changing kaleidoscope of symptoms requires frequent assessment of need and coordination of support services, resulting in identification and availability of a primary person to coordinate coverage and care. When this role falls upon a family member, they are put in the position of having to divide their time, energy and resources and make decisions that often affect the constellation of the whole family. That is why awareness and impact of Alzheimer's disease needs to be understood by all family members, maximizing the likelihood that the family can maintain its balance while providing the aging loved one with the needed critical support.

Summary

Dementia is an unrelenting brain disease that slowly steals one's memory and then moves on to steal one's remaining abilities. At this point in time, there is no cure; just a handful of medications that can slow down the course of decline.

In teaching a young child about the illness and the road ahead, it is best to provide only basic, minimal information. Children will ask if they want to know more. Be reassuring and honest, and let your children express their thoughts. Make sure to say that Alzheimer's is not contagious and that kids don't get it. Permit your child's reactions - whatever they may be - even if they are not what you hoped for. Feel free to share your own feelings if it seems like the right thing to do and, if possible, find a hopeful comment to offer, as small as it may be. You may not know how to respond to some of the difficult questions your child asks and that is to be expected. The following list of tips and resources is provided to help you find some answers.

Tips for Families With Loved Ones Who Have Alzheimer's

- Maintain routines as much as possible. Keep caregivers, schedules, places and activities as consistent as possible. Eliminate clutter but do not rearrange furniture in their room.

- Keep a go-bag with lists of medications, doctors, allergies, names and contact numbers of family members and a change of clothes ready in case hospitalization is needed. You may want to include a single day dose of medication as well.

- Provide identification in necklace or bracelet form in case your loved one wanders and gets lost. The Alzheimer's Association has partnered with **medicalert** to provide a device that contains vital demographic and medical information, as well as family contacts. It notifies the family if the patient has wandered and arranges for their safe return (see Resources).

- Enter phone numbers of designated adults in their cell phone for automatic dialing, especially under ICE (in case of emergency).

- Develop a schedule and identify responsible caretakers to check on them several times a day. A phenomenon known as *sun downing* often occurs in the late afternoon and early evening when those with dementia become more confused.

- Provide social and mental stimulation. Maintaining brain fitness is one of the key factors in delaying the progression of the disease. Reacquaint your loved one with activities they once enjoyed which may have lapsed over time.

- Provide opportunities for physical movement or light exercise. It doesn't have to be a formal, rigorous routine but body movement is important.

- Provide a healthy diet that mainly includes fish, fruits, vegetables, olive oil, legumes, chicken and nuts. Limit consumption of red meat, sugar and fats.

- Label closets, drawers and cupboards with contents.

- Reduce choices (e.g., food, clothing, activities) and demands made upon the person.

- Eliminate the need to correct patients about inconsequential facts. Try to understand the nature of one's comments, even if they use the wrong name, word or sentence fragments, or if they confuse facts and float among topics. Respond to the essence of what they are trying to say rather than the details.

- Patients may repeat the same conversational thread or repeat questions, especially about topics from their early years. If it seems like new information to them, they expect it is probably new for you as well. Your best response would be one that makes their comments feel valued and mirrors their thoughts, even if they are flawed (i.e., "You're remembering a lot of things about your years in the service. That was a very important time in your life" or "There are some things from your childhood that seem crystal clear to you now. Do you want to tell me about them?"). The tone of your voice should not be dismissive and, instead, should reflect that you care.

- Do not use phrases such as, "I already told you," "Like I said...," or "Don't you remember we already discussed this?" The person obviously doesn't recall the information, and expressing your frustration this way feels demeaning and will do nothing to enhance their memory. It is not helpful to make them feel criticized or guilty for their diminishing capabilities and the toll it is taking on you.

- Do not argue or ask them the same questions repeatedly, hoping for a different answer. Find what soothes their deteriorating logic. Research suggests that happiness appears linked to longevity.

- Remember, as frustrating as this is, they are not doing this on purpose. You once relied on them. Now they need you.

- Continue to love them.

Caring for someone with Alzheimer's disease can be a major undertaking that is both stressful and draining. It can also hold false promises, when occasional good days make you wonder if the situation may actually be improving. It is important that you take care of yourself during this trying time and share obligations with others (if you can). It is also important to find oases of enjoyment in your life to balance the strain it creates and to optimize your own brain, body and emotional health. The person with the disease has no choice but to count on others. You are filling a critical need. You are also showing your children the impact of your devotion and care - lifelong lessons they will carry into adulthood.

As I write the closing of this book, I recall my father's words of wisdom at age 103:

"They want you to remember them how they were. Not how they are now."

Questions and Answers

The following questions and answers are offered as possible scenarios which you may encounter. While the answers will obviously not fit all situations, they can serve as a starting point for you to consider a response in advance, should your child ask. They are only a sampling of the wide range of possible replies. You can use them, sculpt them or discard them as you see fit. You know your child best.

Q: What's wrong with Grandma/Grandpa?

A: When people get old, their bodies change. When you were a baby, Grandma had brown hair but now it's mostly gray. Grandma used to walk faster and sometimes even run, but now she walks more carefully. Sometimes she needs us to speak loudly because she might not hear us when we use a regular voice. Can you think of anything else that has changed? These are all things we can see. But inside of Grandma's body, things are changing that we can't see. Her muscles are a little weaker and her brain is changing, too.

Grandma has a disease called Alzheimer's (or dementia) that is making her brain change. The parts of her brain that send messages to each other aren't working the right way and information is getting tangled up in there. Messages for remembering and doing things aren't getting through and there is no way to fix that. There are some medicines that can help slow down the problem, but none that can make her brain go back to the way it was.

Q: Will Grandma/Grandpa get better?

A: When Grandma gets a cold or cuts her finger, those things will get better. But her Alzheimer's won't get better. Alzheimer's will make her confused and forgetful and, as time goes on, it will get worse. Alzheimer's is a mean disease and acts like an enemy. After it mixes up someone's memory, it decides to make them have trouble with other things, like eating, walking and remembering how to get dressed and take care of themselves in the bathroom. Grandma will need help with all those things. Scientists are trying to figure out how to destroy this enemy, but they haven't found the right weapons yet. Maybe, if you like science when you grow up, you can help discover a way to fight this disease!

Q: Does Alzheimer's hurt?

A: No, it doesn't hurt Grandma's body, but her feelings might be hurt, because she knows she can't do the things she used to be able to do.

Q: Can I catch Alzheimer's?

A: Definitely not. It's not the kind of disease that somebody can catch from somebody else. It's the kind of disease that happens to some people's brain all by itself when they get old. But it doesn't happen to everybody. Most people don't get it.

Q: I don't want to see Grandma/Grandpa. Do I still have to visit them?

A: I know you don't feel comfortable seeing Grandma these days because she is so different. It can feel weird. I would love for you to come with me when I go to see Grandma, because she doesn't get many visitors and you can keep me company on the ride there, but if you don't want to come, I understand. You don't have to. Or maybe you can just come in, say "hi" and then leave and go for a walk with Dad while I talk to her. Or perhaps we will both go but only stay a little while. I will leave it up to you. If you decide not to come, maybe you would like to draw a picture or make something out of Play-Doh that I can bring to her when I go.

Q: How come Grandma/Grandpa keeps saying the same things over and over again and calls me by a different name?

A: Alzheimer's is a disease that makes Grandma forget many things that are happening now, but sometimes she will remember random things from a long time ago. Maybe something reminds her of a time or a person from the olden days and maybe that's why. Since she can't remember new things very well, she needs to keep asking. Or maybe she forgot that she told us already, so she tells us again.

Q: What does Grandma's/Grandpa's helper do?

A: Grandpa's helpers try to do the things for him that he has trouble with, like cooking, taking a shower, getting dressed and other things that can be complicated. After a while, Grandpa will have trouble walking and talking, and his helpers will be there for those things when he can't do them by himself.

Q: What should I do when Grandma/Grandpa makes a mistake?

A: If it's a little mistake, don't even tell him. But if it's a big mistake, you can tell him in a nice way. And if you can't tell the difference, you can come and ask me.

Q: I'm afraid of Grandma/Grandpa because they have been yelling a lot. Are they going to be violent or hurt me?

A: Grandpa doesn't mean to be loud and angry, but he doesn't see things the same way we do. Sometimes, he believes things that aren't correct, and other times he can't get things out of his head that upset him. There are times he will become very frustrated because he can't find the words he needs to express himself. If we try to do something for him that he doesn't want, like putting on his jacket, he might fight us on it. He's not trying to hurt us - he's just showing us that he wants us to leave him alone. After a while, he will calm down. I won't ask you to do anything for Grandpa when he is feeling like that.

Q: How come Grandma/Grandpa needs a wheelchair?

A: Our brains are in charge of our whole body. When Grandpa got Alzheimer's, it started to do things like make him confused or moody. But when his Alzheimer's got worse, it started to damage the parts of his brain that are in charge of moving his body. At first, he started to walk more slowly and had trouble with balance, and now he can only stand up with help. But when he is in a wheelchair, he can go anywhere he wants, even faster! So, for Grandpa, it's a good way for him to get around now.

Q: What's going to happen to Grandma/ Grandpa?

A: Grandpa's Alzheimer's will get worse, and he will need more and more help with everything. At first, he will need just a few helpers, but after a while, he will need help all day and all night. He won't be able to live by himself anymore.

Q: Is Grandma/Grandpa going to die?

A: One day he will, just like everything dies when it's their time. But you don't have to worry about that now. I will let you know when I think its Grandpa's time. It's not right now.

References

Alzheimer's Association (n.d.) Dementia vs. Alzheimer's Disease: What is the Difference? Retrieved from https://www.alz.org/alzheimers-dementia/difference-between-dementia-and-alzheimer-s.

Alzheimer's Association Report: 2019 Alzheimer's disease facts and figures (2019, March 1). *Alzheimer's &Dementia 15*(3). Retrieved from https://alzjournals.onlinelibrary.wiley.com/doi/abs/10.1016/j.jalz.2019.01.010.

Alzheimer's Association (2019) Wandering and getting lost: Who's at risk and how to be prepared. Retrieved from: https://alz.org/media/Documents.

Alzheimer's Association Report: 2020 Alzheimer's disease facts and figures. *Alzheimer's &Dementia 2020: 16*: 391-460. Doi:10.1002/alz.12068. Retrieved from wileyonlinelibrary.com/journal/alz

Amazing Advances in Research, Technology, and Patient Care (2018, March 2). Caring for the caregivers: research informs interventions to ease their burden.

Arvanitakis, Z & Bennett, D. (2019, November 5). What is dementia? *Journal of the American Medical Association 322*(17), 1728.

Harrar, S. (2017, December) Avoid Alzheimer's: Understanding your risk factors can stave off memory loss. *AARP Bulletin 58*(10), pp. 16.

Herndon, J.R. (2019, June, last reviewed). Alternative Staging System for Alzheimer's: Reisberg's Stages. Retrieved from https://alzheimersdisease.net/reisbergs-stages/.

Ingram, V. (2003, July-August). Alzheimer's Disease. *American Scientist, 91*(4), 312-321.

Kivipelto, M. & Hakansson, K. (2017, April). A rare success against Alzheimer's. *Scientific American, 316*(4), 32-37.

Kluger, J. & Sifferlin, A. (2018, February 26). How to live longer, better*. *Time, 191*(7-8), 47-50.

Mayo clinic. *Dementia.* Mayo Foundation for Medical Education and Research (MFMER). Retrieved from https://www.mayoclinic.org/dfiseases-conditions/dementia/symptoms-causes/syc-20352013?p=1.

Munson, M. (2017, December). Guard your memory. *AARP Bulletin, 58*(10), pp.15.

Park, A. (2010, October 25). Alzheimer's unlocked. *Time, 176*(17), 53-59.

Park, A. (2016, February 22-February 29). Alzheimer's from a new angle. *Time, 187*(6-7), 64-70.

Park, A. (2018, February 26). Please be the drug. *Time, 191*(7-8), 54-63.

Sifferlin, A. (2016, February 29). It's the little things. *Time, 187* (6-7), 80-86.

Smith, G. (2016, May-June). Healthy cognitive aging and dementia prevention. *American Psychologist, 71*(4), 268-275.

The National Academies of Sciences, Engineering and Medicine- news release (2016, September 16). New report calls for systemwide reorientation to account for health care and support of both elders and family caregivers.

Weir, K. (2017, July-August). Keeping Dementia at Bay. *Monitor on Psychology, 48*(7), 46-5.

Information Resources

Alzheimer's Association www.alz.org   or email: adear@nia.nih.gov
National office: 225 N. Michigan Avenue Fl 17, Chicago Illinois 60601-7633 phone: (312) 335-8700   fax: (1866) 699-1246

Alzheimer's 24/7 hour helpline   (1800) 272-3900

National Institute on Aging   www. nia.nih.gov/Alzheimers (1-301) 496-1752 (1-888) 722-6468

Alzheimer's Disease Neuroimaging Initiative www. adni-info.org

Safe Return Resources

Safe return hotline: www.alz.org/ResourceCenter/Programs/Safereturn.htm (888) 572-8566

24/7 Wandering Support for a Safe Return: https://www.alz.org/help-support/caregiving/safety/medicalert-with-24-7-wandering-support

Safe Return Program. www.verywellhealth.com/alzheimers-safe-return-program: medicalert.org/alz or medicalert.org/safereturn   or www.alz.org/safereturn

The Safe Return enrollment form comes in English, Chinese and Spanish. They provide identification labels for clothes, wallet cards and identification bracelets as well as notification to family members when there is a problem.

About the Author

Laurie Zelinger and her dad at age 103.

Dr. Laurie Zelinger is a board-certified psychologist with a specialty in school psychology, and a Registered Play Therapist with over 45 years' experience. She is a licensed New York State psychologist who, after retiring from a Long Island public school system, is now devoting her time exclusively to writing, consulting and her busy private practice for children. Previous books include: *Please Explain Anxiety to Me: Simple Biology and Solutions for Children and Parents*; *Please Explain Tonsillectomy & Adenoidectomy to Me: A Complete Guide to Preparing Your Child for Surgery*; *Please Explain Terrorism to Me! A Story for Children, P-E-A-R-L-S of Wisdom for Their Parents*; *Please Explain Time out to Me! A Story for Children and Do-it-Yourself Manual for Parents;* and *A Smart Girl's Guide to Liking Herself Even On The Bad Days* for American Girl.

In June 2020, Dr. Zelinger's article, "Expanding social stories beyond the autism spectrum" was a featured article in *Play Therapy* magazine. She has a chapter on selective mutism in the John Wiley & Sons compendium *School Based Play Therapy*, as well as a chapter on prescriptive play therapy for fears and phobias in the 2019 Guilford Press compendium, *Prescriptive Play Therapy: Tailoring Interventions to Specific Childhood Problems*. Dr. Zelinger is also credited with being a consultant for the Bitty Baby book series by American Girl where she assisted in the development of the 'For Parents' sections as well as editorial development of another American Girl book. Her interest in writing began in 4th grade, when a play she wrote about the drought experienced in New York City at the time, was performed by the students in her public school.

Dr. Zelinger is a fellow and previous officer in the national American Academy of School Psychology and had spent four years in the capacity of director on the executive board of the New York Association of Play Therapy. As a highly respected child psychologist, she has contributed to nearly 200 venues regarding child development. She and her psychologist husband, Dr. Fred Zelinger, are both certified Red Cross disaster mental health volunteers. They have been happily married for over 40 years, have raised four children and relish their roles as grandparents.

CPSIA information can be obtained
at www.ICGtesting.com
Printed in the USA
BVHW011152050523
663651BV00023B/872

9 781615 995912